THE

INTERNATIONAL LIBRARY

OF

PIANO MUSIC

ALBUM TEN

THE
INTERNATIONAL LIBRARY
OF
PIANO MUSIC

Advisory Board

SISTER ALICE MARIE, O.S.U.

LEONARD BERNSTEIN

VAN CLIBURN

AARON COPLAND

OLIVER DANIEL

NORMAN DELLO JOIO

ROBERT DUMM

WALTER HENDL

PETER MENNIN

ROBERT PACE

RUDOLF SERKIN

ROGER SESSIONS

HALE SMITH

CLAUDETTE SOREL

Editorial Staff

FELIX GREISSLE
Music Director and Editor-in-Chief

CORINNA MARSH
Literary Editor

ARNOLD BROIDO
Associate Music Editor

ELIZABETH VOLDSTAD
Assistant Music Editor

1969

THE UNIVERSITY SOCIETY, Inc.
Educational Publishers since 1897
New York

In addition to its wealth of contemporary material, this *new* INTERNATIONAL LIBRARY OF PIANO MUSIC combines the most successful teaching and playing masterpieces of its predecessors; namely:

TECHNIQUE

(STUDIES AND EXERCISES)

compiled and edited

by

DENES AGAY

FOREWORD

Albums Ten through Thirteen *(Technique)* are designed to help students develop a well-rounded technique. Besides the instructive etudes of Czerny, Clementi, and Cramer, we have also included, for specific study purposes, compositions by Bach, Handel, Shostakovitch, Bartok, and Kabalevsky. There is also a varied selection of exercises and a clear presentation of the basic scales and arpeggios.

Both the *Table of Contents* at the front of each album and the alphabetical index at the back of Album Thirteen provide easy access to this wealth of material.

Technique begins with simple studies in five finger position and progresses to the difficulties of bravura octaves and chords. Because of their progressive arrangement, their broad scope and balance, the *Technique* albums can be used as a foundation for the teacher's personal method or as supplementary material.

Practiced intelligently and consistently, these etudes, exercises, scales, and arpeggios will promote both sound musicianship and technical expertise.

TABLE OF CONTENTS

in order of studies

ALBUM TEN

GLOSSARY OF TECHNICAL TERMS

arpeggiated chord A chord with the notes played rapidly from the bottom up. Its sign is a wavy line ({) placed in front of the chord.

arpeggio, grand Broken chord extending to two or more octaves.

arpeggio, small Broken chord moving within the span of the octave.

articulation Manner of separating or binding together notes. *See also* **phrasing, legato, staccato, tenuto, non legato.**

broken chord A chord in which the tones are sounded not simultaneously but one after the other in any order. *See also* **arpeggiated chord, arpeggio.**

cantabile In a singing manner. Often applied to a smooth, well emphasized performance of a melody line.

close figures Figures involving all five fingers within a span of less than a fifth.

contrary motion The hands proceeding in opposite directions, either towards or away from each other.

divided chord A chord divided into two parts sounded alternately.

double notes Two notes played simultaneously with one hand.

finger action The finger moving as a unit from the hand.

five finger position A position in which the fingers are placed on five consecutive keys of a major, minor or modal scale.

forearm rotation A rotary motion of the forearm, wrist, and hand turning alternately clockwise and counter-clock-wise from the elbow.

forearm action The hand, wrist, and forearm moving up and down from the elbow.

heavy arm The weight of the arm is transferred to the fingers and keys.

high finger action The finger strikes the key from a distance higher than usual, for a distinct and firm touch with clear separation of tones. Used mostly as a drill for developing the strength, independence, and coordination of the fingers.

legato A smooth, connected manner of playing. The depressed key is not released until the next key is struck; there is no gap or interruption between the two consecutive tones. **Legatissimo:** superlative of *legato*, a very smooth, connected manner of playing.

leggiero A light non-legato touch usually applied in faster passages. It requires a light arm and very resilient finger action. **Leggieramente:** superlative of *leggiero*, a very light, fast manner of playing.

light arm Arm weight is not transferred to the fingers. It is used in both legato and staccato playing and is indispensable for any *leggiero* touch.

non legato Somewhere between *legato* and *staccato*. The tones are detached and somewhat separated but not sharply so.

parallel motion The hands proceeding in the same direction at a given interval.

phrase A melodic unit, the most important building block of musical form.

phrasing The shaping and linking together of musical thoughts into phrases. Phrasing can be compared to the observance of punctuation marks in a sentence.

portato A singing *non legato* touch in which every tone receives a slight emphasis. It should be distinguished from the often erroneously used *portamento*.

staccato A short, detached, crisp manner of playing. The key is released immediately after depression, the exact length of each tone depending on note value and tempo. **Staccatissimo:** the superlative of *staccato*, a very detached and crisp manner of playing.

syncopation A displacement of the natural accent within a measure which occurs in the music of all periods, and lends a rhythmic individuality to certain types of folk music and jazz.

tenuto The notes are sustained for their full time value, perhaps even a shade longer. This term does not imply any tempo change and should not be confused with *sostenuto*.

touch The manner and speed with which the key is depressed and released, and the tone which is produced.

tremolo A rapid alternation of two notes at an interval larger than a second, a double note and a single note, or two double notes. See also **divided chord.**

trill A rapid alternation of the written note and the note above or below it. Can be performed by pure finger action or fingerwork combined with a slight forearm rotation. Preliminary exercises should stress all feasible finger combinations on the same two notes, for instance: 1-2, 1-3, 2-3, 2-4, 3-4, 3-5, 4-5, then 3-5, 3-4, 2-4, 2-3, 1-3, 1-2.

wrist action The hand moving as a unit from the wrist.

STUDIES IN FIVE - FINGER POSITION

Legato in **both** hands

Cornelius Gurlitt

NOTE: *After playing the above studies as written, it is suggested that they be practiced in other keys.*

2

Half notes against whole notes, legato in both hands

Louis Köhler

5

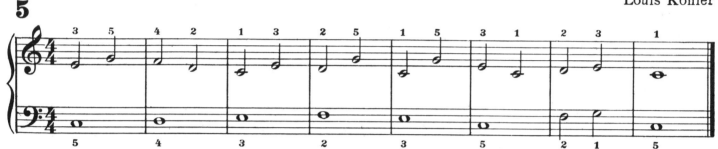

Half notes and whole notes in parallel and contrary motion, legato in both hands

6

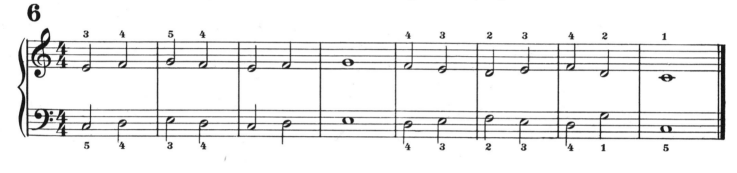

7

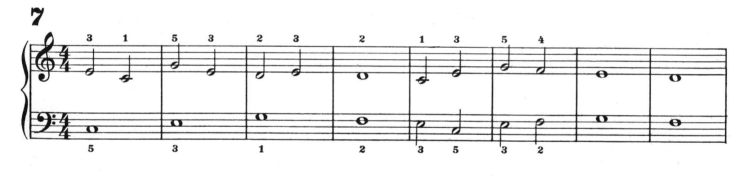

8

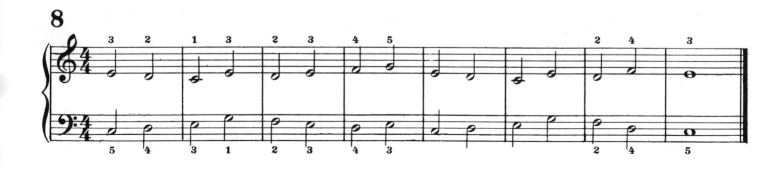

Quarter notes against whole notes; legato in both hands

Cornelius Gurlitt

Repeated notes

Carl Czerny

4

Legato phrases; the dotted half note

11

Louis Köhler

Legato phrases; the tie

12

Ferdinand Beyer

THREE PIECES FOR LEGATO PHRASING; DYNAMIC SHADING

I

Charles Dennée

6

Legato; high finger action; the eighth note

Louis Köhler

16

Legato eighth note figures in alternating hands

Louis Köhler

17

Moderato

Finger staccato

Louis Köhler

18

Finger staccato, legato and tenuto

19

Louis Köhler

20

Louis Köhler

Wrist staccato

21

Karl Urbach

Wrist staccato; tenuto; melody divided between the hands. Use third finger only.

22

Elena Gnesina

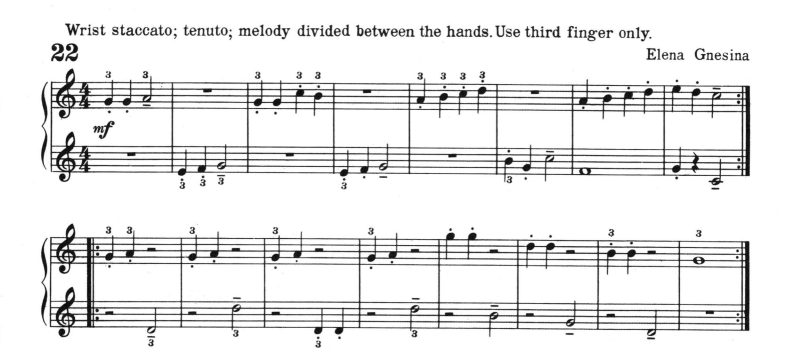

8

Five finger legato melody; ties and slurs

23

Charles Dennée

IMITATION

24

Anton Krause

Five finger legato in unison; shifting hand positions

Béla Bartók

25

Even five finger legato on different dynamic levels

Ferdinand Beyer

26

Moderato

Legato in shifting five finger positions

Cornelius Gurlitt

27

FIVE STUDIES FOR THE INDEPENDENCE OF HANDS

Charles Dennée

TWO STUDIES FOR THE INDEPENDENCE OF HANDS

33   I   Ferdinand Beyer

34   II   Ferdinand Beyer

THREE LEGATO STUDIES IN BROKEN INTERVALS

35 I — Ferdinand Beyer

36 II — Ferdinand Beyer

14

Oct. 21

III

Ferdinand Beyer

37

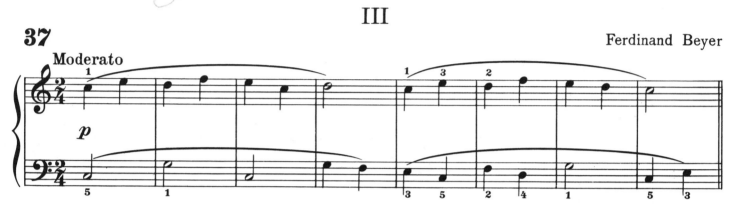

Study in $\frac{6}{8}$ time

38

Folk Song

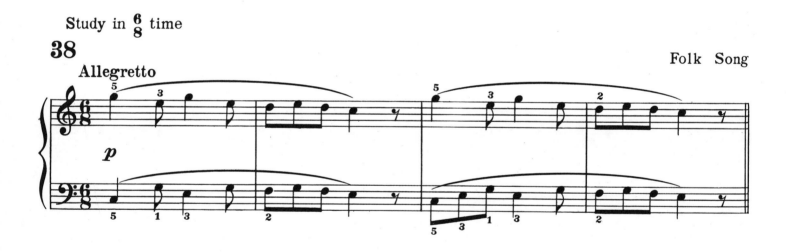

Preparatory study for forearm rotation

39

Louis Köhler

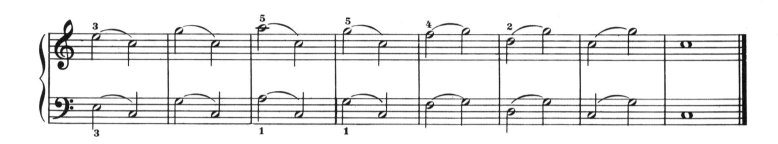

Quiet five finger legato; slightly rotating forearm

40

Anton Krause

Rotation study

41

Ferdinand Beyer

Allegretto

LITTLE SCHERZO

Finger staccato; parallel motion in both hands; shifting five finger positions; slight rotation

42

Dmitri Kabalevsky

Animato

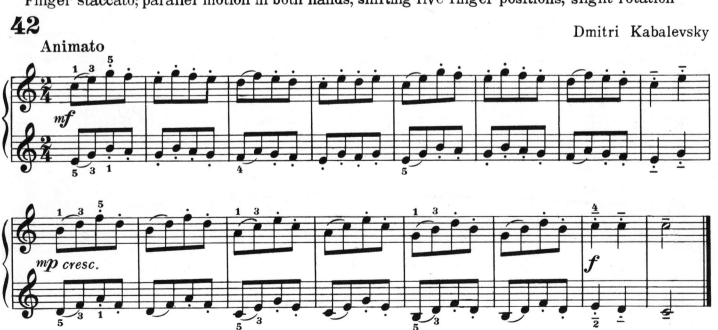

ANSWERING VOICES
Five finger legato

43

Charles Dennée

44

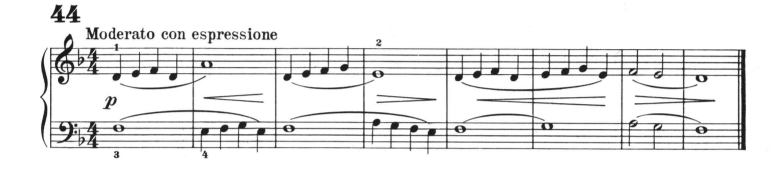

THREE LITTLE CANONS

45

Charles Dennée

46

47

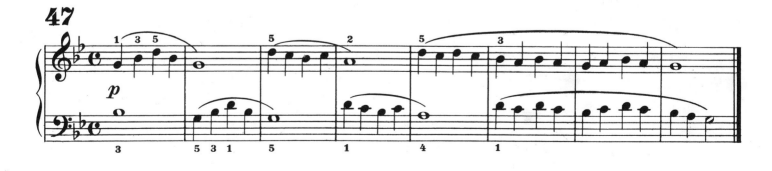

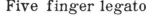

TWO STUDIES FOR ALTERNATING LEGATO AND STACCATO TOUCH

Carl Czerny

48

I

49

II

Carl Czerny

TWO LEGATO STUDIES

I

Charles Dennée

II

Charles Dennée

51

Moderato

Legato study for even touch; shifting left hand positions

52

Louis Köhler

THREE DUETS

Secondo

I

Ferdinand Beyer

53

THREE DUETS

Primo

I

Ferdinand Beyer

Pupil's Part

53

Andante

II

54

Allegretto

55

Andante

TWO LEGATO STUDIES

Hands in different positions

56   I   Charles Dennée

Moderato

Contrary motion

57   II   Charles Dennée

Allegretto

Thirds in right hand; both notes should be sounded at exactly the same time

Carl Czerny

58

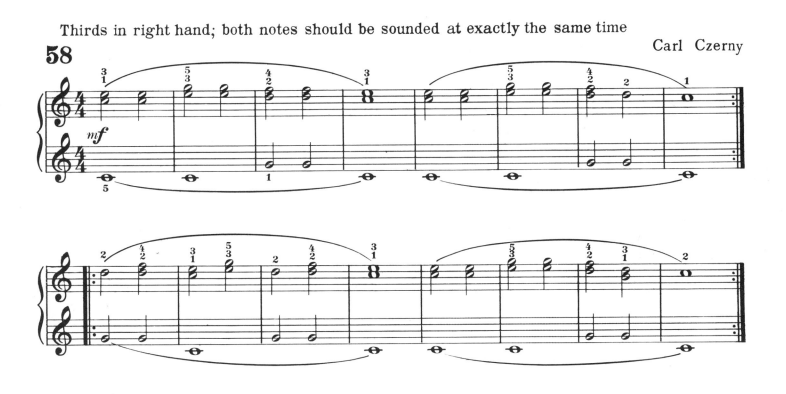

Legato thirds in five finger position

59

Louis Köhler

Moderato

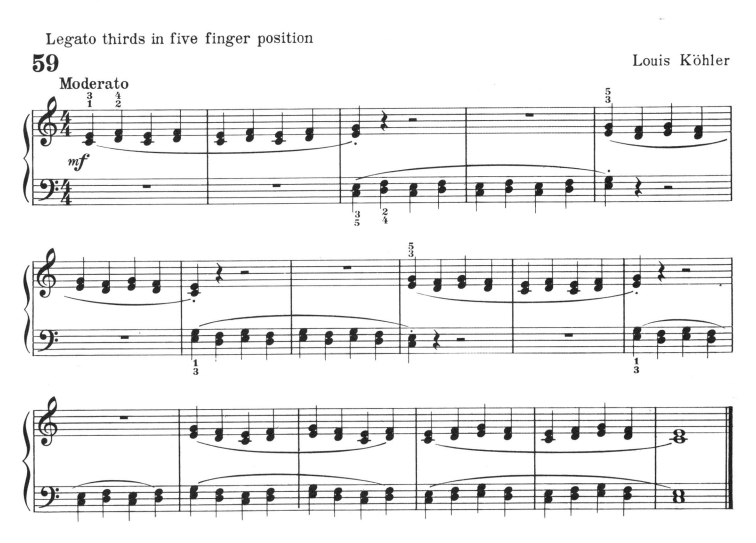

FIVE - FINGER POSITION
with occasional extensions of the playing range

Legato thirds

Ferdinand Beyer

60

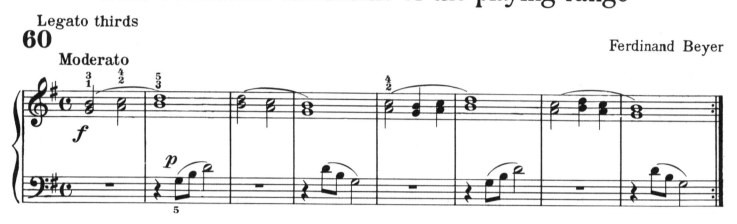

61

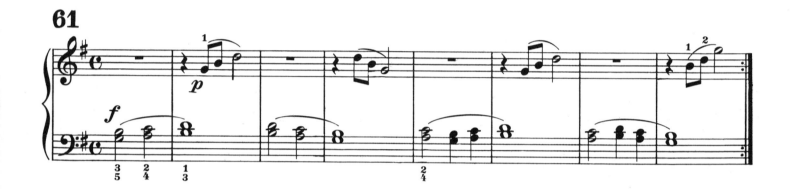

62

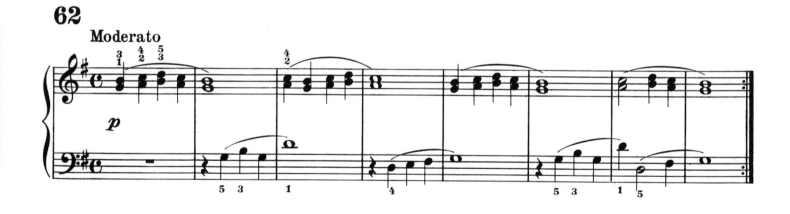

63

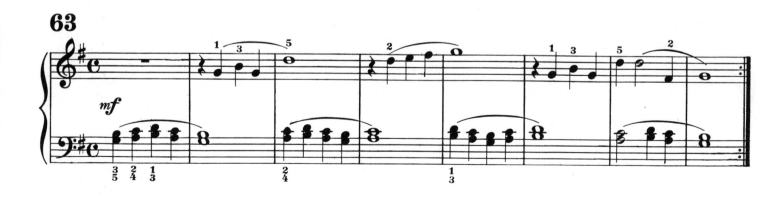

Staccato thirds

64

Elena Gnesina

Three note slurs; double notes in left hand

65

Cornelius Gurlitt

Staccato and legato touch; double notes in left hand

66

Karl Urbach

Moderato

Contrasting touch; legato and staccato

Louis Köhler

67

Contrasting touch; imitation

68

Elena Gnesina

Moderato

STUDIES IN NOTE VALUES
Leger lines in the bass staff

Charles Dennée

THEME AND VARIATIONS

Legato; high finger action.

A. E. Müller

74

Allegro moderato

Variation I

33

Variation II

Variation III

Five finger legato with trill-like figures

Charles Dennée

75

76

Charles Dennée

EIGHTH NOTE FINGER EXERCISES
Increase speed gradually

77

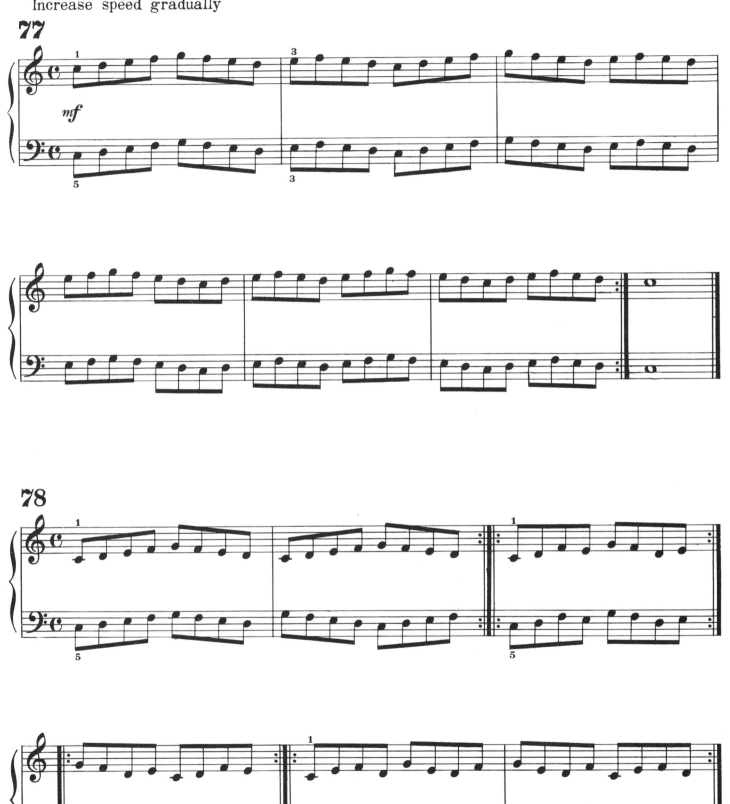

78

THEME AND VARIATIONS

Study in note values and non legato touch

79

Johann Hummel

Variation VI

Studies in note values and rhythmic precision

Anton Krause

80

Allegro

81

Allegro

38

FINGER EXERCISES

For rhythmic practice and the development of facility

The following exercises should be practiced with both hands together after they are well learned separately. Play slowly, with accurate lift and stroke of the fingers, keeping them curved at all times.

Count four equal beats in each measure.

Practice and learn *one* exercise at a time; do not try several at once.

82

83

Intervals of seconds and thirds

84

85

86

Rhythmic variants

87

88

TWO STUDIES
For independence of hands

I

Anton Krause

89

Allegretto

II

90

Anton Krause

Allegretto

STUDIES IN TRIADS
in four keys
C major

91

Carl Czerny

Moderato

F major

92

E♭ major

93

A major

94

43

Broken triads

95
Charles Dennée

Allegro moderato

96
Carl Czerny

Allegretto

Repeated chords in left hand; shifting five finger position

Anton Krause

97

Allegretto

Legato thirds

98

Gustav Damm

Legato and staccato thirds; wrist action

99

Carl Czerny

Broken triads; rotation

Charles Dennée

100

Moderato

STUDIES IN EXTENDED PLAYING RANGE

Two-note legato slurs alternating between the hands

Cornelius Gurlitt

101

Legato broken triads, smoothly and evenly alternating between the hands

102

Louis Köhler

Moderato

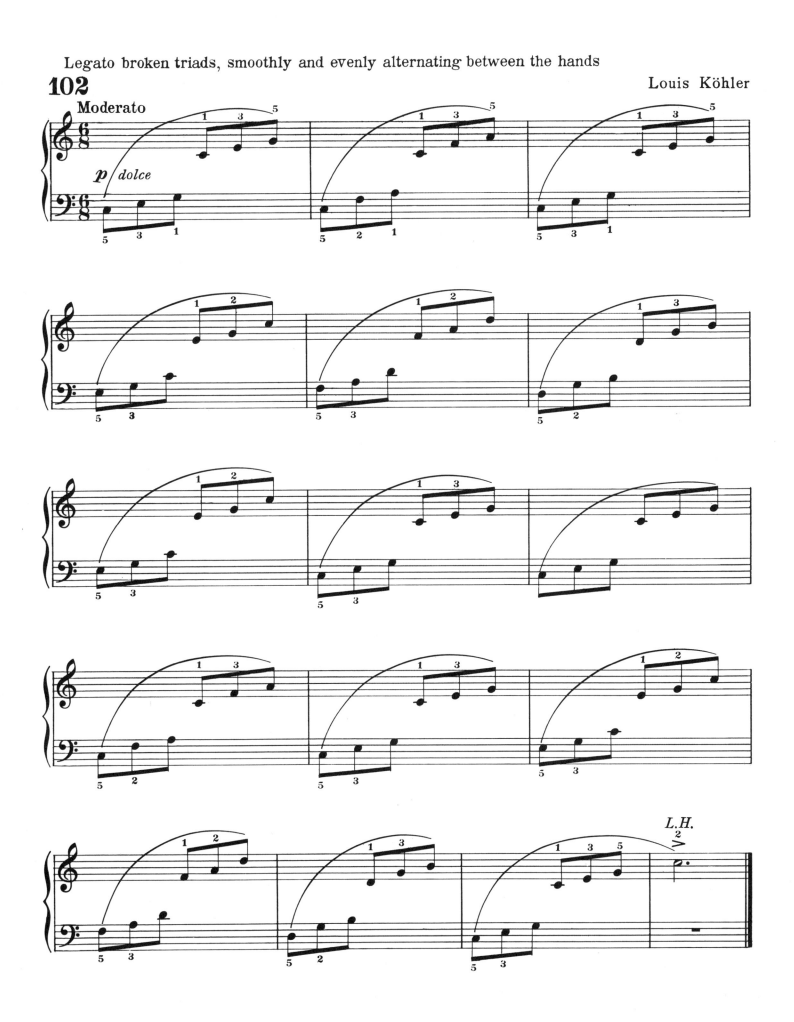

TWO ARPEGGIO STUDIES
Arpeggios divided between the hands; play them evenly as if performed by one hand.

Ludwig Schytte

I

103

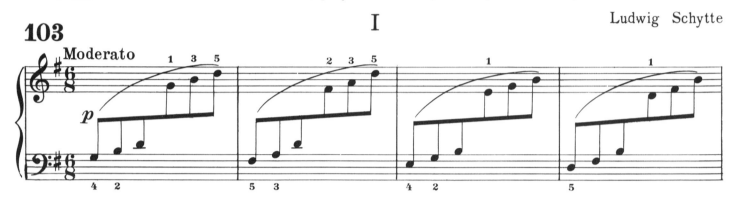

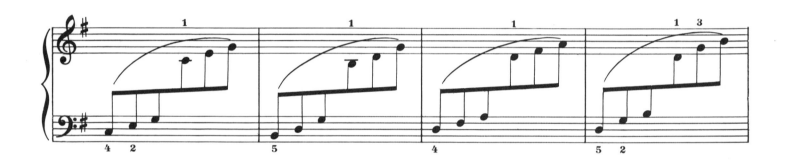

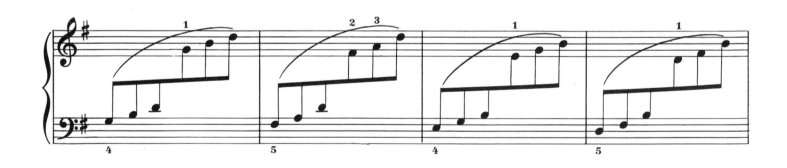

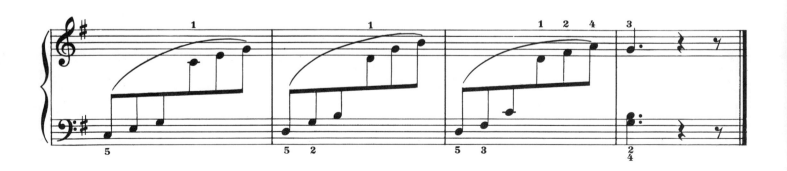

II

104

Ludwig Schytte

52

Smoothly alternating broken triads

105

Jean Duvernoy

Broken chord patterns divided between the hands

M. Ossokine

106

THREE STUDIES
Dotted quarter and eighth note patterns

Divided chord accompaniment

109

III

Ferdinand Beyer

Comodo

Divided chord accompaniment

110

Carl Czerny

Allegretto

57

Solid chords and divided chords

111

Con moto

Carl Czerny

Staccato repeated chords

112

Karl Urbach

Allegro moderato

Legato repeated chords; melody in left hand

113

Arnold Sartorio

Allegretto

Syncopated melody

114

Henri Bertini

Lento

p legato

Broken and divided chord patterns

115

Louis Köhler

Allegretto moderato

Repeated notes and double notes; non legato

116

Cornelius Gurlitt

Allegretto

Wrist staccato; single and double notes

117

Cornelius Gurlitt

Allegretto

GERMAN FOLK SONG

118

Louis Cramer

Syncopated melody; solid chord accompaniment

119

Henri Bertini

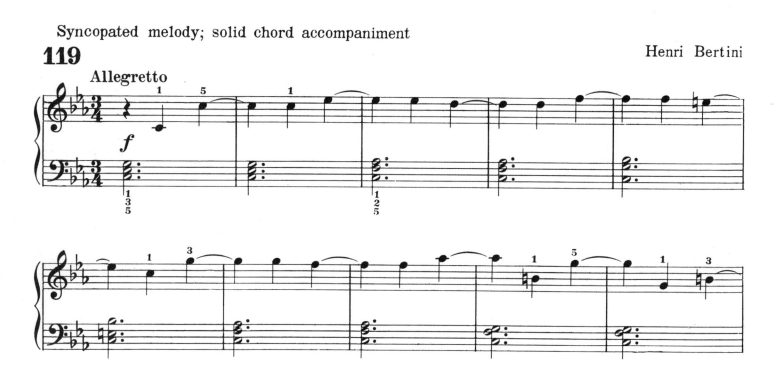

Chords divided between the hands; bring out melody notes.

120

Ludwig Schytte

Cantabile playing, with pressure touch in right hand; play left hand broken triads with a light **arm** and slight rotation.

Louis Köhler

121

Right hand cantabile

122

Moderato

Cornelius Gurlitt

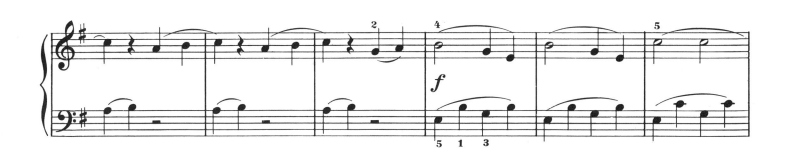

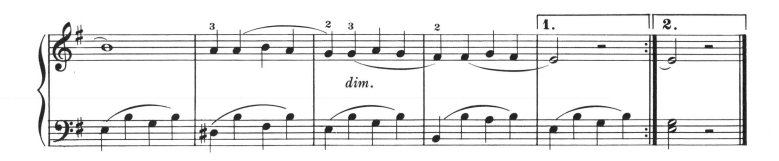

TWO STUDIES WITH TRIPLETS
Legato in both hands

123

I

Ludwig Schytte

Allegretto

MARCH

124

II

Ludwig Schytte

BROKEN TRIADS
Moving through the positions in succession
C major

125

Pupils with large hands may also practice this fingering: $\frac{R.H. \quad \underline{123 \quad 124 \quad 124 \quad 123}}{L.H. \quad 321 \quad 421 \quad 421 \quad 321}$ This prepares the hand for the broken chords of four notes, C E G C, G C E G, in which 1st, 2nd and 5th fingers are always used, with a choice between the 3rd or 4th finger according to the interval. Fundamentally, if the interval is a fourth, play with the 3rd and 5th fingers; if it is a third, play with 4th and 5th fingers.

When well under control, extend these exercises to a compass of two, three and four octaves.

69

STUDY IN MOTION
Broken triad passages; rotation of forearm

Charles Dennée

126

Comodo

Alternating broken triads

127

Charles Dennée

Staccato broken triad figures

128

Heinrich Wohlfahrt

Allegro scherzando

ROLLED OR ARPEGGIATED TRIADS

The triad should be rolled or quickly broken from the lowest to the highest note. It is like the effect produced when chords are played upon a harp; hence the term "arpeggiated" or "harp-like."

129

Andante

Charles Dennée

129 a

Moderato

Contrasting touch in the two hands

130

Christian Koehler

Allegro moderato

THE CUCKOO

Staccato and legato touch

Christian Koehler

131

Allegretto

TWO LEGATO STUDIES
Legato five note figures to promote evenness of touch in the fingers

132   I   Ludwig Schytte

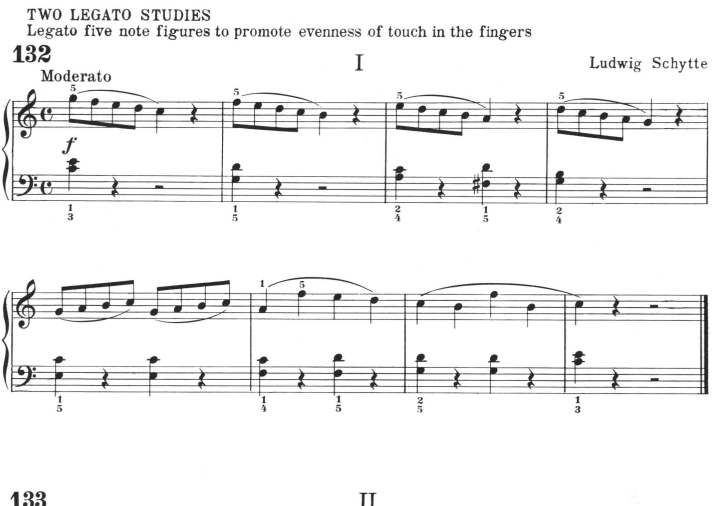

133   II   Ludwig Schytte

THE FIRST SCALE STUDIES

Legato scale passages divided between the hands

Alexander Goedicke

134

Vivace

Preparatory exercise for passing under of the thumb

Elena Gnesina

135

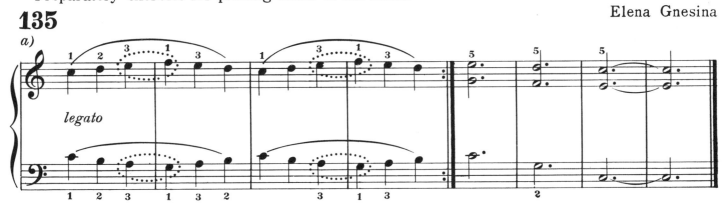

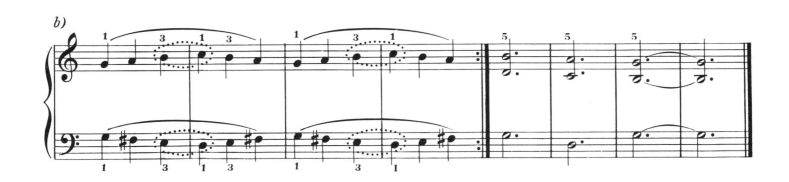

MAJOR SCALES

136

When the scale is learned so that it can be played easily and fluently, practice it in the following manner:

Also the reverse, starting with the 5th finger in each hand:

‖: 5 4 3 2 1 3 2 1 :‖‖: 2 1 2 3 1 2 3 4 :‖

SCALES WITH THE HANDS TOGETHER

When the scales are well learned with separate hands, they should be played with the hands together. Do not play the scales in parallel motion until they are first thoroughly mastered in contrary motion. In scales in contrary motion the same fingers play at the same time in both hands, which makes it much easier to learn and to establish correct habits of fingering. Continue the practice of the preparatory exercises for scale playing even after the scales have become easy to play. Technique is a means to an end. Technical development should always be in advance of the requirements of the pieces.

Write the scales in all keys, using this model:

137

After writing the following scales, write the correct key signatures and the proper fingerings. Write and practice one scale at a time.

G major

R. H.

L. H.

D major

R. H.

L. H.

A major

R. H.

L. H.

E major

R. H.

L. H.

F major

R. H.

L. H.

TWO STUDIES
For evenness in simple scale passages

138   I

Moderato   Henri Lemoine

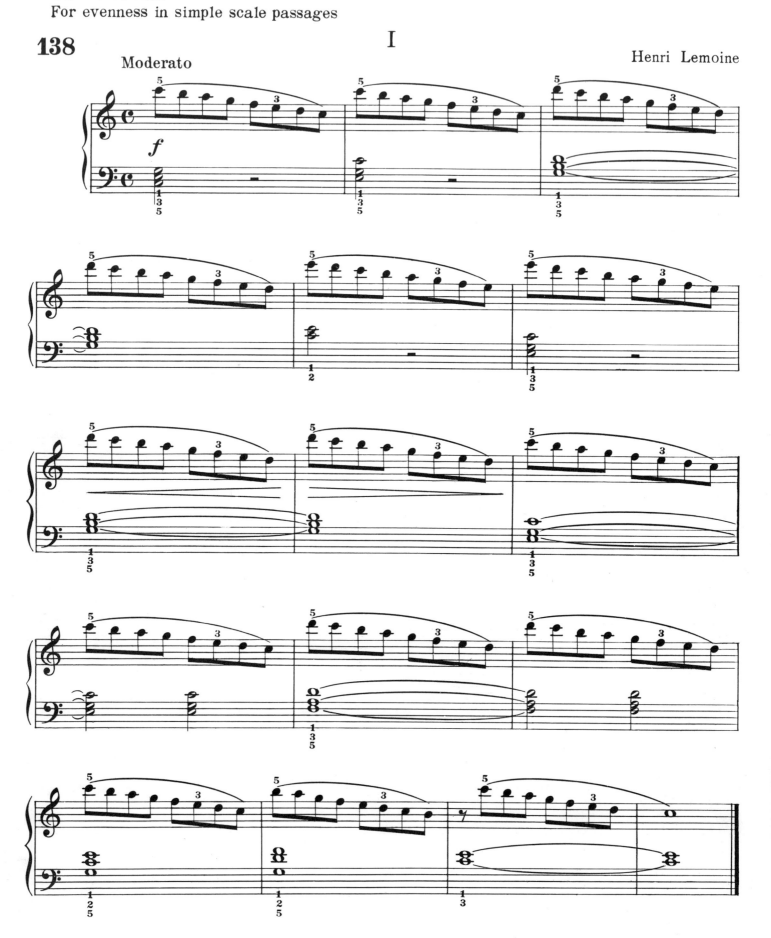

II

Moderato

Henri Lemoine

139

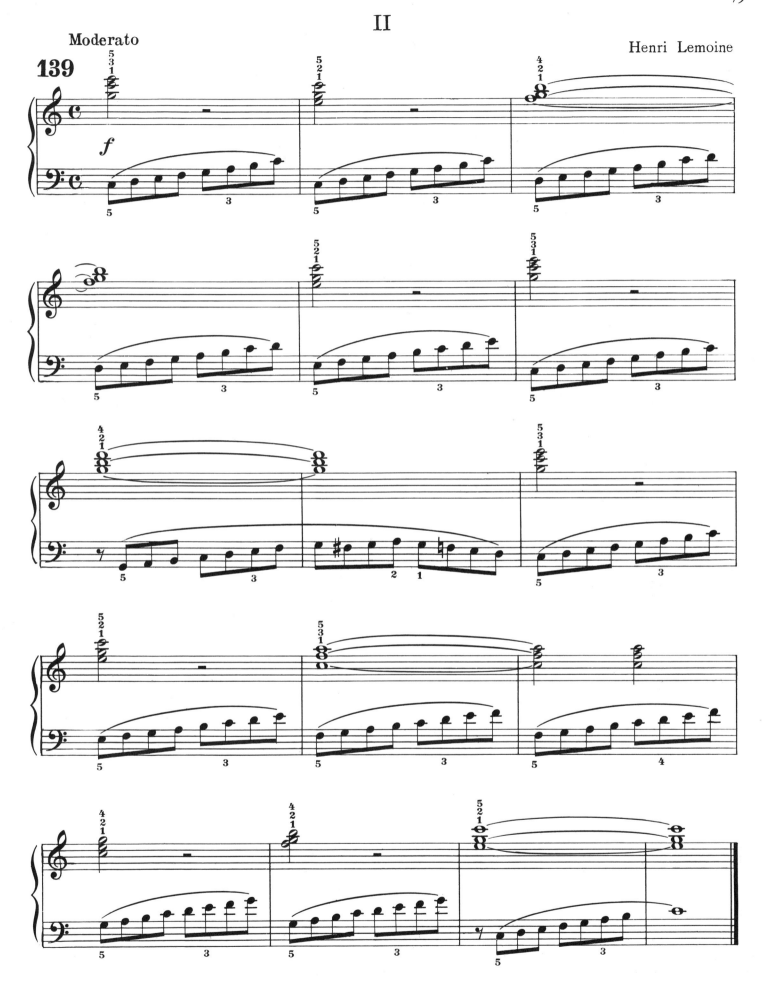

TWO SCALE STUDIES

140   I   Gustav Damm

Moderato

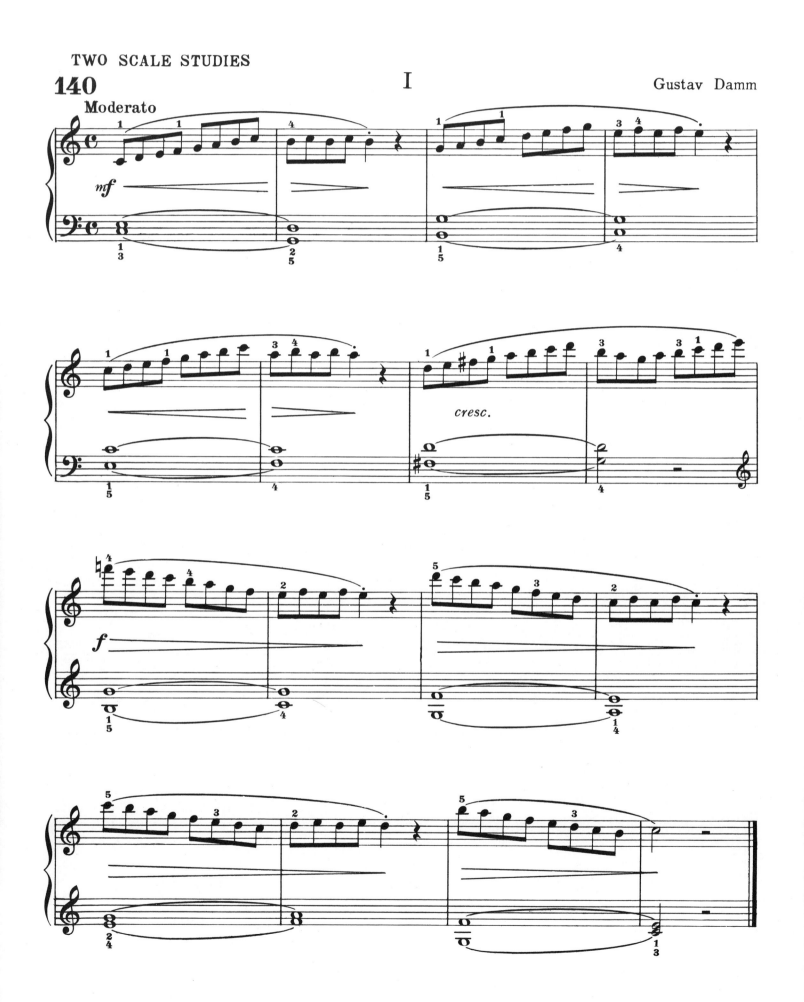

II

141

Gustav Damm

Legato figures and passages alternating between the hands

Ferdinand Beyer

142

Comodo

TWO ARPEGGIO STUDIES

FIRST FORM OF THE ARPEGGIO

143

Play the left hand an octave lower. Do not stiffen or strain the hands.

SECOND FORM OF THE ARPEGGIO

144

84

TWO ARPEGGIO STUDIES
Play with a light forearm, rotation, and a firm touch.

I

145 Moderato

Carl Döring

II

146

Carl Döring